GEOLOGY
of the
North York Moors

—— Contents ——

Text and Photographs (except aerial): Alan Staniforth
Design: Gillian Sunley

Front cover photograph
Far Jetticks from Clock Case Nab, north of Robin Hood's Bay

© North York Moors National Park Information Service July 1993
ISBN 0 907480 21 7

Diagrammatic Section through the North York Moors

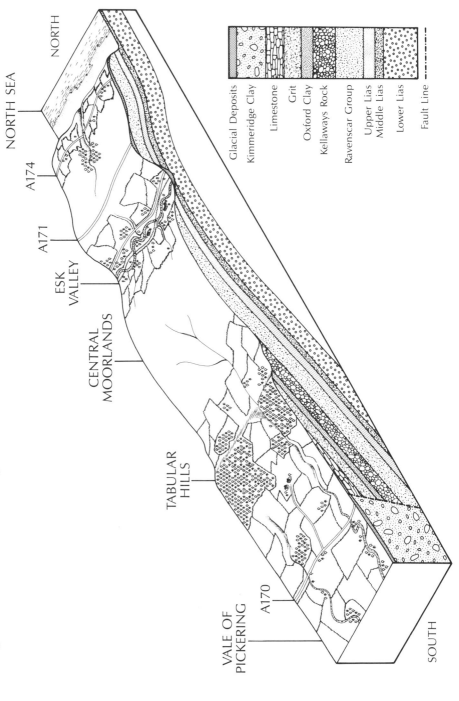

NORTH

NORTH SEA

A174

A171

ESK VALLEY

CENTRAL MOORLANDS

TABULAR HILLS

A170

VALE OF PICKERING

SOUTH

Glacial Deposits

Kimmeridge Clay

Limestone

Grit

Oxford Clay

Kellaways Rock

Ravenscar Group

Upper Lias

Middle Lias

Lower Lias

Fault Line

Foreword

Many visitors to the North York Moors come to the area to enjoy the scenery. Through a selection of photographs this guide explains how the rocks beneath our feet influence the land over which we walk.

Man's effect on the landscape is also briefly explained, particularly where mining and quarrying have scarred the cliffs and hillsides.

With the exception of aerial shots, all the photographs have been taken from public rights of way, the exact location is given as a map reference in the photo caption.

Introduction

"In no part of England is the relation of the surface topography to the nature of the underlying rocks more instructively displayed than in this district. The strata being nearly horizontal and little disturbed by dislocations, the valleys radiating from the tableland can be traced out as the results of erosion with a precision and completeness unattainable in other parts of the country where the geological structure is less simple." (Sir Archibald Geikie, 1898)

"The region forms one of the most natural divisions of Yorkshire possessing its own special physical boundaries." (Frank Elgee, 1912)

These two quotations written at the turn of the century by a geologist of international standing and an eminent local archaeologist, serve to indicate the unique nature of the North York Moors National Park.

Not only the shape of the land but also the sandstones and limestones used in local building give an indication of the nature of the rocks to be found in the area. The quarries, many now abandoned, the crags along the valley sides and the magnificent coastal scenery all serve to display both the rock type and structure of the region.

A knowledge of the underlying rocks of any area help us not only to understand the shape of the land but often to account for the nature of the land use and reasons for the siting of farms and villages.

PART 1

——— Rocks and Relief ———

To many people the sheer number of rock types and their often unusual geological names leads to confusion and lack of interest in geology. This confusion need not arise if we realise that there are three principal classes into which all rocks may be divided:

1. Igneous rocks
Rocks cooled from a molten state, e.g. granite or basalt.
2. Sedimentary rocks
Rocks compressed from sediment, e.g. sandstone or shale.
3. Metamorphic rocks
Originally igneous or sedimentary rocks which have been dramatically altered by intense heat and/or pressure, e.g. marble or schist.

With one exception, all the rocks forming the North York Moors belong to the sedimentary class and were deposited in seas or river deltas that covered this area during the Jurassic period. Deposition of the Jurassic sediments began 213 million years ago and continued for 63 million years. The youngest rocks in the area are thus 150 million years old with the exception of the injection, 58 million years ago, of a stream of molten lava into the rocks of the high moors. Today this forms the Cleveland Dyke or Whinstone Ridge.

Although there are many different types of sedimentary rocks in the area, they may conveniently be divided into four groups, with the oldest at the bottom.

> Kimmeridge Clay Group
> Middle Oolite Group
> Ravenscar Group (Deltaic Series)
> Lias Group

Lias Group maximum thickness 440 metres (1443 feet)

The word Lias comes from the Gaelic "leac" meaning a flat stone which aptly describes the almost horizontal layers which build up the series.

Over 400 metres of Lias rocks are exposed in the area but, due to the folding and faulting of the rocks, nowhere is a complete

Ravenscar and Blea Wyke

Looking south from below the Raven Hall Hotel (980025)

Below the Raven Hall Hotel, built on the site of a Roman signal station, the cliffs fall 180 metres (600 ft) to sea level. A complete sequence of strata from Upper Lias on the shore to beds of the upper Ravenscar Group in the cliff top are exposed. Large blocks of sandstone litter the shore and the platform in the foreground.

The distant headland of Blea Wyke is formed from seaward-dipping resistant strata of late Lias – early Oolitic age.

The word 'Wyke', in common use on the Yorkshire coast, is of Scandinavian origin meaning a narrow coastal inlet.

— 5 —

vertical section visible. The upper and lower beds consist of a compact grey shale with occasional outcrops of impure limestone. The middle beds contain more sandstones and ironstones which have been extensively worked in the past, particularly around Staithes and the valley of the Murk Esk. The Lias was originally deposited as fine silt and mud on the bed of a deep sea and the rocks now contain a large number of fossilised remains of creatures which lived in that sea.

Easily eroded, the Lias outcrops along the coastline from Redcar to Ravenscar, often capped with younger sandstones of the Ravenscar Group (Deltaic Series). Inland, streams have cut through the sandstone capping to carve broad valleys into the Lias shale below, for example in Rosedale, Farndale and Eskdale.

Towards the close of the Lias period, the sea became shallower and a deposit was laid down which eventually formed the Dogger, an ironstone extensively worked in the nineteenth century, particularly in Rosedale and the Cleveland Hills.

Ravenscar Group (Deltaic Series) maximum thickness 250 metres (820 feet)

As the sea shallowed even more, conditions changed, resulting in the area being covered by a great river delta. Sand and mud deposited at this time were later compressed and today form the sandstones and shales of our high moorlands. It is the massive sandstones of this series which produce the crags which attract climbers, particularly in the northern part of the park. The same sandstone has been used extensively for building in the area. On three occasions during its existence, the ancient delta was invaded by the sea. This resulted in the formation of rocks differing from the sandstones and containing fossil forms of marine origin. The thickest, and most interesting of these marine deposits is called the Scarborough Formation or Grey Limestone. Outcropping in moorland valleys and on parts of the high moor, as well as on the coast, this rock gives rise to interesting local variations in vegetation, lime loving plants often appearing in an area otherwise dominated by acid moorland. The Scarborough Formation is not immediately recognised as a limestone due to its dark grey and often sandy appearance and, perhaps for this reason, is often overlooked.

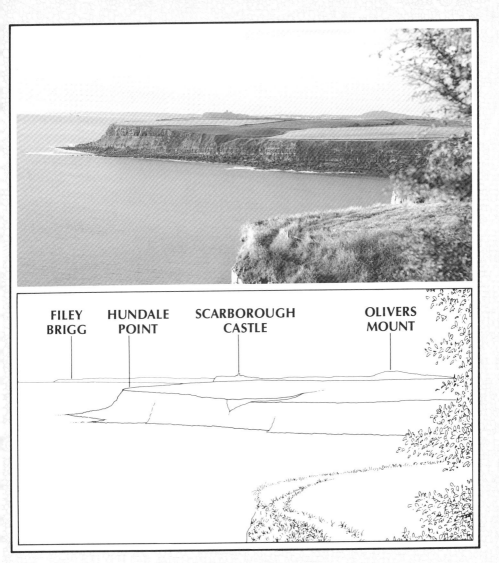

Cloughton Wyke

Looking south from the Cleveland Way (020952)

Bedded sandstones and shales dipping to the south-east can be clearly seen on the south side of Cloughton Wyke. The rocks all belong to the Ravenscar Group, their variable hardness giving rise to the typical cliff profile seen at Hundale Point.

In the distance the faulted headland (Middle Oolites) on which Scarborough Castle stands is visible. To the west is Oliver's Mount, also of Middle Oolitic age, and part of the Tabular Hills. On a clear day, the long, low promontory of Filey Brigg may be seen, with the chalk cliffs of Speeton and Flamborough beyond.

Middle Oolite Group maximum thickness 200+ metres (656+ feet)

The deposition of the Ravenscar Group was brought to a close by a fourth marine invasion from which the delta never recovered. This was the beginning of a period during which alternating layers of sandstones, clays and limestones were deposited in warm, generally shallow seas. Many of the limestones were oolitic, consisting of tiny rounded grains about the size of a pin head. Each grain, or oolith, has a nucleus such as a sand grain or piece of shell, around which layer upon layer of lime has been deposited. When all the ooliths become cemented together the rock is said to be oolitic. The principal beds of the Middle Oolite, in ascending order, are Kellaways Sandstone, Oxford Clay, Lower Calcareous Grit, Coralline Oolite and Upper Calcareous Grit. It is the rocks of the Middle Oolitic sequence which today form the Tabular and Hambleton Hill ranges extending from Scarborough through to Helmsley and the south western escarpment. The Tabular Hills terminate in an impressive north facing escarpment overlooking the high moors.

Kimmeridge Clay Group maximum thickness 225 metres (738 feet)

The final representatives of the Jurassic period in north east Yorkshire are a thick series of very fossiliferous clays. These rocks form the low ground of the Vale of Pickering and are only exposed in several clay pits near Kirkbymoorside. Thought to have been deposited in seas of increasing depth, the Kimmeridge Clays have become very well known in recent years due to the many boreholes for gas, water and oil which have passed through the group.

—— Evolution of a Landscape ——

Following a break in deposition at the close of the Jurassic era, the area was again covered by seas in which chalk was deposited. The chalk has since been completely eroded from the North York Moors but still forms the Yorkshire Wolds to the south. During the last 65 million years north east Yorkshire, which had for the previous several hundred million years been

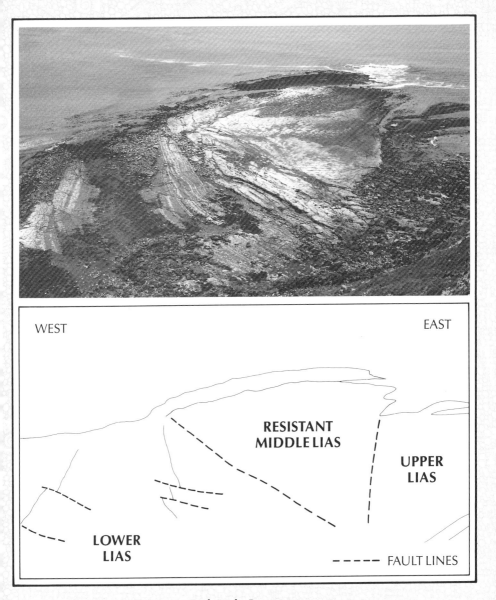

WEST

EAST

RESISTANT MIDDLE LIAS

UPPER LIAS

LOWER LIAS

– – – – – FAULT LINES

Peak Fault, Ravenscar

Looking north from below Ravenscar golf course (980025)

Geological faults occur at several places along the Yorkshire coast and these have often resulted in the formation of headlands.

At Ravenscar, a major fault has allowed a wedge-shaped piece of resistant Middle Lias to become sandwiched between less resistant rocks to east and west. This complicated fault system is clearly visible at low tide. Smaller lateral faults can also be seen dislocating the reefs of Lower Lias to the west.

— 9 —

under water, was uplifted to form land. During the period of uplift, North Yorkshire behaved very much as a rigid block. The layers of rock were tilted only very gently and can be seen today in much the same horizontal attitude as that in which they were laid down. Rocks in the southern area of the park dip gently southwards, particularly in the Tabular Hills. In the northern districts many gentle domes and basin structures occur, a good example of an eroded dome being at Robin Hood's Bay. Faults, or breaks in the rocks occurred round the margins of the block, particularly in the coastal areas and along the southern section of the Tabular Hills.

Ice, rain, wind and sea have, for millions of years, eroded the rocks to produce the forms we see today. The same processes are still operating particularly along the coastline which is eroding at an average rate of 5 centimetres (2 inches) a year.

—— Fossils ——

Fossils are the remains, or traces, of once living animals or plants that are found naturally embedded in the rocks. The oldest known animal fossils are found in rocks which are over 600 million years old while the youngest date from only a few thousand years before the present time. Fossil remains are only found in rocks which were originally soft sediments, deposited usually, though not exclusively, under water. When animals living in ancient seas died, their remains fell to the sea floor where the soft parts often decayed. Shells and skeletal remains gradually became covered with sand or silt and as the sediment was compressed so the remains became fossils. Similarly, plants, washed into the sea from the surrounding land, became buried under sediment. Though soft, the leaves, stems and seeds underwent a chemical change which resulted in their being turned into carbon. A study of fossils can tell us a great deal, not only about the animals and plants themselves, but about the conditions in which they lived.

Practically all the rocks which form the North York Moors are sedimentary, many of them deposited in deep or quiet seas where current action was minimal. Such conditions were ideal for the preservation of fossils and hence the area has long been famous for its range and numbers of fossils.

The period during which our local rocks were formed is often referred to as the "Age of the Ammonites". A soft bodied tentacled animal, the ammonite lived in a flat, coiled shell which was divided into compartments. As it grew the animal constructed a new and larger compartment into which it moved, thereby extending the size of its shell. Locally, ammonites range in size from a fraction of an inch up to nearly 60 centimetres (2 feet) in diameter and show a bewildering variety of forms. Some have a keel along the outer edge, others carry patterns of bumps or knobs and many show varieties of ribbing. These varied characteristics enable geologists to identify differing species and to establish a system of classification. Because of their similarity to a coiled snake, ammonites were, until about 150 years ago, regarded as such. Saint Hilda, the first abbess of Whitby Abbey is said to have been plagued by snakes in her abbey until she cut off their heads and threw them over the cliff where they curled up and turned into stone! The Latin name for one of the common ammonites is *Hildoceras bifrons* and Whitby has incorporated three of these into its town crest. The fossil remains of marine reptiles such as *Plesiosaurus* are still occasionally found in the Lias shales and many museums in the country display specimens collected from Yorkshire during the eighteenth and nineteenth centuries. The Whitby Museum displays some particularly fine specimens collected during this period.

A study of fossils shows that while advanced forms of life eventually became extinct, the simpler forms often survive through many geological periods. In fact, many fossils found in local shales and limestones are distinctly similar to species living today. Good examples are the whelks, scallops, and razor shells.

The ancient delta, in which the local Deltaic Sandstones were formed, was not a favourable area for the preservation of fossils due to the strong current action and coarseness of the sediment. Those fossils which are preserved, however, are particularly interesting. Plant remains produce thin seams of coal while single specimens appear as sooty imprints in the sandstone, often showing very fine detail. Leaves from the Maidenhair tree (*Ginkgo*) and stems of Horsetail (*Equisetum*) are found which closely resemble living species. Technically, a fossil may be only a trace left in the rock by an animal or plant. Into this category fall the dinosaur footprints for which this part of Yorkshire is famous. Three toed reptiles walking over the mud banks of the ancient delta would often leave behind the impression of their feet, which, under favourable circumstances, were preserved.

Glacial History

About 2 million years ago, a change in climatic conditions led to the onset of the Great Ice Age. The polar ice caps spread many miles beyond their present positions and local ice caps became established in many mountain areas. Land that was not covered by ice or water became a frozen waste from which animals had migrated and in which plants died or seeds became dormant. During the Great Ice Age there were several advances of the ice between which warmer conditions prevailed. The most recent cold period existed until about 10,000 years ago when warmer conditions returned, the ice melted to its present limits and animals and plants colonised the land once again.

While the highlands of Scotland, the peaks of the Lake District and parts of the Pennines developed local ice caps, the North York Moors, because of their lower elevation, became an area of snowfields and tundra. The ice sheets, spreading from the mountain areas, pushed up against the west and northern escarpments of the moors and against the eastern seaboard, surrounding the North York Moors on three sides. The effect this ice had upon the edges of the moorland was quite dramatic and though the ice has long since disappeared, the evidence for its former existence is still very clear.

This evidence falls broadly under one of two headings. Firstly, evidence in the form of glacial boulder clays, sands and gravels which were left behind when the ice melted; and secondly, the meltwater channels or spillways formed when water from one glacial lake flowed into another or escaped from the ice front.

As the later ice sheets did not cover the high moors, it is along the fringes where we expect to find the concentration of glacial deposits. The sticky brown clay which plasters our coastline is a good example of the debris left by the melting ice. For many years regarded as a rather mixed-up and uninteresting deposit, the boulder clay is now the subject of much detailed research. A study of its deposition can tell us a great deal about the nature of the ice while the erratic blocks which it contains are valuable guides to the origin of the ice. While certain types of rocks have a very wide distribution, others are restricted to a particular area. When samples of such localised rocks are found at considerable distances from their source, and can be proved

Meltwater Channel – Fylingdales Moor

Looking west from the A171 road (943005)

During the last Great Ice Age much of the North York Moors was surrounded by huge ice sheets. Because the North Sea was itself blocked with ice, meltwater could not flow seawards but coursed away from the ice – often in directions totally opposed to normal drainage patterns.

The A171 Scarborough – Whitby road crosses several of these meltwater channels which now show little if any evidence of a stream flowing through them.

Cleveland Dyke

Looking north-west from Sil Howe (853028)

The Cleveland Dyke or Whinstone Ridge is the only igneous rock to occur, in situ, within the park. Intruded as a molten lava 58 million years ago, the line of the dyke runs from Great Ayton to Fylingdales Moor.

The hard, black volcanic rock has been quarried and mined for roadstone at several localities along its course. At Sil Howe the now partly filled quarries can be seen extending down towards the Esk Valley. Large mines were also worked beneath Sil Howe until their closure in 1950.

Newton Dale Gorge

Looking north from Skelton Tower (820929)

Newton Dale is undoubtedly the most dramatic valley which cuts through the North York Moors National Park. From its head at Fen Bog near Fylingdales until it opens into the vale near Pickering it displays a sinuous course often between sheer cliffs several hundreds of feet high. In its size and grandeur it is unlike any other valley in the moors.

Recent research suggests that this dramatic gorge was cut, probably in only a few decades, by vast quantities of water draining a glacial lake and ice sheet in the Esk Valley. This occurred around 10,000 years ago towards the close of the Great Ice Age when much of Britain was covered by huge ice sheets.

Forge Valley and Hackness

Aerial photograph looking north-west from 989857. (Crown Copyright)
The broad Hackness Valley, carved from the Tabular Hills by spring sapping and stream erosion, contrasts with the narrow, steep-sided Forge Valley in the foreground. Forge Valley was cut during the last Ice Age by water overflowing from a glacial lake ponded up in the Hackness Valley.

The upper, steep slopes of the hills in the Hackness Valley are largely wooded and correspond to the poorer soils developed on the Calcareous Grit Formation. The farmland on the hilltops results from the better quality limestone soils, while the rich land on the floor of the valley is derived from river and old lake deposits. The sides of Forge Valley, being very steep, are tree covered irrespective of the underlying soil and rock.

The River Derwent which previously flowed out to sea along the Sea Cut Valley (extreme right centre) was diverted in glacial times and today flows through Forge Valley to the Vale of Pickering. In the early 19th century an artificial cut was constructed to carry flood water from the Derwent to the sea at Scarborough. The Sea Cut can be seen as a straight line running diagonally across the upper centre area of the photograph. Towards the top of the picture is the village of Hackness.

to have been transported by ice, they serve as valuable guides to the direction of ice movement. Examples of such erratics found on the Yorkshire coast are Shap Granite from the Lake District, Schist from Scotland and Rhomb Porphyry from Scandinavia.

It is difficult for us to imagine ice sheets, hundreds of feet in thickness, virtually surrounding the North York Moors. Such thicknesses of ice prevented streams and rivers reaching the lowlands and so the water accumulated in many of the moorland valleys to form glacial lakes. This occurred principally in the upper Esk Valley and the Hackness Valley near Scarborough. When the rising water reached the lowest point in the surrounding hills, it overflowed and drained away from the lake, often in directions totally opposed to normal drainage patterns. When the ice disappeared, many of these channels were left dry, or at best, with only a small stream to occupy them. Good examples are to be seen in the Goathland area. Newtondale Gorge and Forge Valley near Scarborough display the most dramatic features and are undoubtedly two of the best examples of meltwater channels in the country.

—— Quarrying and Mining ——

Bronze Age man was probably the first to exploit the local rocks about 4,000 years ago. Jet jewellery has been discovered in ancient burial mounds and there is no doubt that early man worked jet which he probably collected from the shore. The first commercial exploitation of the rocks commenced in the early medieval period with the discovery of iron in the Cleveland Hills.

In the early 17th century the mineral alum was discovered in the Upper Lias Shales. Over the next 300 years, millions of tons of shale were quarried from the Cleveland Hills and the coastline in order to extract alum which had important uses, particularly in the tanning and dyeing industries. The industry finally ceased in the 1870s, largely as a result of the development of a method for obtaining cheaper alum from colliery waste. The huge quarries and pink coloured slag tips from the old alum works can still be clearly seen in the northern areas of the national park.

The Cleveland Escarpment

Carlton Bank from 505037

This bold escarpment rises to nearly 300 metres (1000 ft) from the fertile Vale of York. The whole sequence of Liassic strata may be encountered though it is only the Upper Lias which is exposed in the old alum quarries towards the top of the hills. The hard capping of the hills is formed from sandstones of the Ravenscar Group.

The discarded pink, burnt shale from the huge alum quarries is visible for many miles. A line of small depressions running along the contour about two-thirds of the way up the slope marks a series of old jet workings.

Immediately below the Alum Shale lies the Jet Rock, hence, below many of the alum quarries and wherever the Jet Rock outcrops, the entrances to old jet mines may be found. Jet, a form of fossilised wood, can be readily carved and polished and has been used as decorative jewellery since Bronze Age times. Commercial exploitation began during the early nineteenth century and reached its zenith in the 1870s. The industry was centred on Whitby where over 1,500 people were employed in over 200 jet workshops. Unlike alum, jet is still worked in Whitby though the mines have long since closed and the raw material is once again collected from the shore.

It may be difficult today to appreciate that from about 1850 until well into the present century, the northern part of the moors was an area of intense mining activity. This was centred around the ironstone of the Middle Lias and the Dogger. Rosedale was the scene of some of the greatest activity and while many of the scars have healed, remains of buildings, kilns and routes of the old ironstone railways may still be seen. In Rosedale, ore was calcined close to the mines in order to reduce the impurities, and therefore the weight, before it was transported to Middlesbrough for processing. The low quality of the Cleveland iron ores hastened the decline of the industry after 1920 in competition with foreign ores of higher quality. The last mine to operate, North Skelton, closed in 1964.

The massive sandstone of the Ravenscar Group has been used for building stone for many years. Numerous quarries, many now overgrown, may still be seen in the district. Large country houses usually drew their stone from a nearby quarry opened for the purpose. The rock cut readily into convenient blocks and the better quality stone was much sought after. Large quarries were opened near Whitby from which stone was transported for the construction of such buildings as Covent Garden Market, the old Waterloo Bridge and the Houses of Parliament. The limestones of the Tabular Hills have also served as building material, both for houses and the many drystone walls to be seen in that area.

Amongst other valuable materials worked in the district were moorland coal seams within the Ravenscar Group, whinstone for road stone from the Cleveland Dyke and limestone from which agricultural lime and road stone are still obtained.

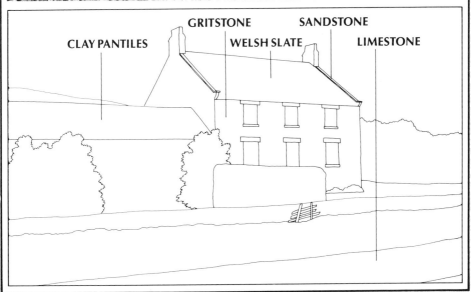

CLAY PANTILES   **GRITSTONE**   **SANDSTONE**

WELSH SLATE   **LIMESTONE**

Mowthorpe Farm, Hackness (981884)

Local geology is clearly reflected in the past use of building materials. Limestone was used in the south of the park, for cottages and drystone walls, while sandstone and grit was used for larger houses and barns. In the north, sandstone replaces limestone as the main building stone. Red clay pantiles have virtually replaced thatch as roofing material. Welsh or Lake District slate used on some larger buildings was introduced with the development of the railway system in the 19th century.

Geological Map of the North York Moors

Glacial and other superficial deposits are not represented on this map.

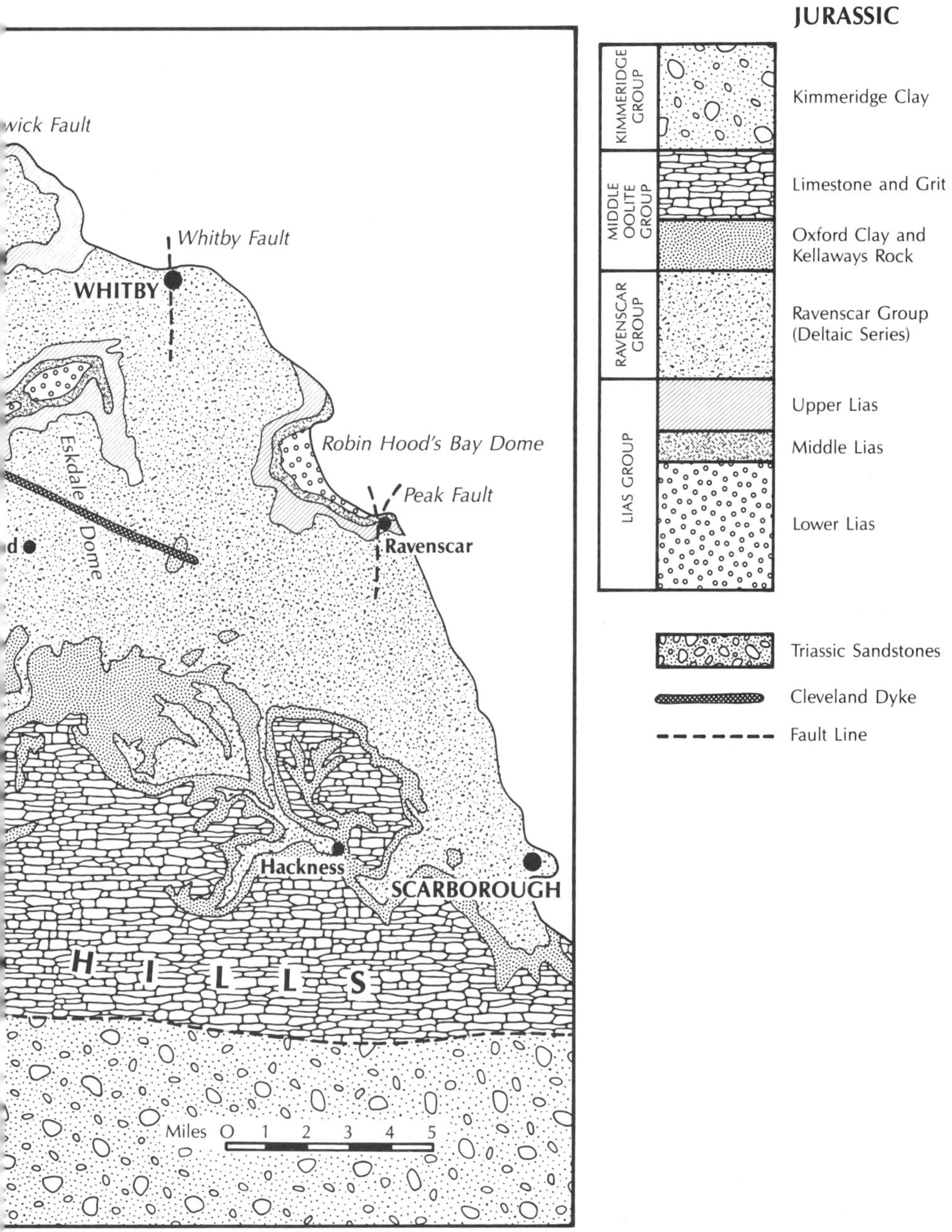

JURASSIC

KIMMERIDGE GROUP		Kimmeridge Clay
MIDDLE OOLITE GROUP		Limestone and Grit
		Oxford Clay and Kellaways Rock
RAVENSCAR GROUP		Ravenscar Group (Deltaic Series)
LIAS GROUP		Upper Lias
		Middle Lias
		Lower Lias

Triassic Sandstones

Cleveland Dyke

- - - - - - - Fault Line

wick Fault

Whitby Fault

WHITBY

Eskdale Dome

Robin Hood's Bay Dome

Peak Fault

Ravenscar

Hackness

SCARBOROUGH

H I L L S

Miles 0 1 2 3 4 5

The latest in the long history of extractive industries centred in the park is the exploitation of the potash reserves north of Whitby. The potash salts, which are valuable to agriculture, are found at depths of up to 1,200 metres (4,000 feet) in rocks of Permian age. These rocks form the foundations of the North York Moors and were deposited as salt lakes evaporated under desert conditions which existed in this region around 270 million years ago, before the Jurassic period commenced.

Boulby Cliff

Looking north-west from Cowbar (775188)

At 210 metres (690 feet) Rock Cliff is the highest sea cliff on the east coast of England.

The upper cliff is composed of massive sandstones, while below, the full thickness of Upper and Middle Lias is exposed with the Lower Lias forming the base of the cliff. The almost horizontal layers of strata are clearly visible with the more resistant beds forming small ledges in the cliff face.

Nearby, Staithes lies in the shelter of Cowbar Nab, formed from the resistant Middle Lias.

Close by to the south is Britain's only potash mine which is working Permian salt deposits down to a depth of 1200 metres (4000 ft).

PART 2

—— The Coastal Boundary ——

In the early years of the 19th century, when the science of geology was beginning to gain in popularity it was to the Yorkshire coast that many students turned to unravel the problems of the strata and their fossil content. Now famous names, amongst them William Smith, Adam Sedgwick, Roderick Murchison and John Phillips are all associated with this coastline. This was no chance association, for between the River Tees and Flamborough Head is displayed an almost complete sequence of rocks from two major geological periods - the Jurassic and the Cretaceous. Excellent exposures, rich fossil beds and comparatively easy access still make this a popular area for amateur and professional geologist alike.

To generalise, it can be said that at Redcar in the north are exposed some of the oldest rocks in our district, the Lower Lias strata. Working south down the coastline one passes gradually up the geological sequence through younger and younger strata until, at Flamborough Head, the upper beds of the Cretaceous System are exposed.

The coastline has been gradually wearing away for several million years and the process is continuing. Perhaps the most noticeable effects are seen where the works of man abut the cliffs, particularly at Staithes, Runswick Bay and Robin Hood's Bay. The wide wave-cut platforms (at Robin Hood's Bay extending at low tide to 600 metres), undercutting of the cliff face and frequent cliff falls are all indications of an eroding coastline and are particularly well seen between Redcar and Ravenscar.

The irregular, indented line of the cliffs is a direct result of the variety of rock types and their differing hardnesses. The headlands all result from resistant strata although their structures may differ. North Cheek at Robin Hood's Bay is a good example of a headland formed as a result of seaward dipping resistant strata (Middle Lias). The same explanation applies to Blea Wyke Point (Dogger) and Hundale Point (Scarborough Formation). At Cowbar Nab, Staithes, the resistant Middle Lias is broken by a pattern of joints at right angles. This has given rise to the dominant flat fronted face of the headland. At Ravenscar geological faulting has resulted in resistant strata (Middle Lias) being moved to sea level, the reefs thus affording protection to softer rocks in the area. At several locations (Kettleness,

Robin Hood's Bay

Looking north-west from Ravenscar (978024)

At a low tide in Robin Hood's Bay, a magnificent wave-cut platform extends seawards for 550 metres (600 yards) from the base of the cliffs. The gradient of this platform varies between 1:75 and 1:100 and is only interrupted by the edges of thin, resistant limestones giving rise to a series of miniature scarp and dip slope features.

The great crescent shaped reefs or scars as they are known locally, are all that remain of a huge geological dome structure centred on the Bay. As the sea has gradually eaten into this structure the successive layers of the dome have been exposed. The distant headland of North Cheek, formed from resistant seaward-dipping Middle Lias rocks, represents the northern edge of the ancient dome.

The Lower Lias cliff line is heavily plastered by glacial deposits from which erratics have been eroded to form extensive pebble beaches.

Sandsend Ness

Looking north from Sandsend (860130)

Many headlands along the Yorkshire coast show features which would be difficult, if not impossible, to describe in terms of the normal processes of erosion. A knowledge of local history is necessary in order to explain the shape of Sandsend Ness, Kettle Ness or Saltwick Nab.

In the early years of the 17th century, the mineral alum was discovered in the Lias shales of Cleveland. Alum was an important commodity in the textile and leather industry and so alum shale was exploited at many coastal and inland localities. The alum industry finally ceased in this part of England about the year 1871, after nearly 300 years of operation.

The quarries at Sandsend Ness opened in 1607 and finally closed in 1867. During that time millions of tons of cover-rock were removed to expose the alum shale which was then removed in vast quantities.

Sandsend Ness, Saltwick Nab) alum quarrying during the 17th to 19th centuries has resulted in massive quantities of Upper Lias shale being removed. This has dramatically altered the cliff profiles of these headlands.

While the coastline has been dominated by erosion, extensive deposition of glacial clays and sands (Boulder Clay) took place during the Great Ice Age. These deposits "plaster" the solid rocks of the coastline often to considerable thicknesses. It is from the subsequent erosion of these clays that the extensive pebble beaches of Robin Hood's Bay result.

—— The Tabular Hills ——

Extending from Scarborough in the east to Helmsley in the west and forming the southern boundary of the moors are the Tabular Hills. Named by Professor Phillips in the 19th century because of their very conspicuous flat tops, these hills rise at a shallow angle from the Vale of Pickering and form a prominent north facing escarpment overlooking the central moorlands. A number of the valleys in the Hackness and Allerston area are the result of spring sapping but the majority of streams which drain the Tabular Hills follow a drainage pattern which was initiated on the smooth surface (peneplain) of the newly uplifted Cleveland Hills. Stream erosion has given rise to the irregular scarp face with its distinctive "nabs" or promontories projecting onto the central moorlands. Excellent views of this escarpment may be seen at Hackness near Scarborough, at Saltergate on the A169, at Lastingham and above Helmsley.

The Tabular escarpment is gradually though imperceptibly wearing away to the south. As this process continues isolated hills are occasionally left behind and wear away more slowly. Such outliers form the conspicuous hills of Blakey Topping at Saltergate and Howden Hill near Hackness. The Hole of Horcum, also near Saltergate, is the result of extensive spring sapping at a location where the strata form a shallow depression.

From the northern scarp face the hills dip gently southwards to the Vale of Pickering, the strata (Middle Oolites) giving rise to farming on the lower limestone slopes while the grits on the

Blakey Topping

Looking east from near Saltergate (866933)

Blakey Topping is one of several small isolated hills within the North York Moors, other examples being Roseberry Topping, Freebrough Hill and Hood Hill. These hills are all referred to as outliers because of their now isolated position in relation to a nearby escarpment. The structure of these hills indicates that they were once a part of the nearby escarpment from which they have since become detached as a result of the processes of erosion.

Hole of Horcum

From the A169 above Saltergate (858939)

This great circular hollow in the Tabular Hills has been caused largely by extensive spring action at the grit-clay junction. Folklore, however, has a different explanation. A local giant by the name of Wade is said to have scooped up a handful of earth and flung it over his shoulder in a fit of rage; thus creating the Hole of Horcum and nearby Blakey Topping!

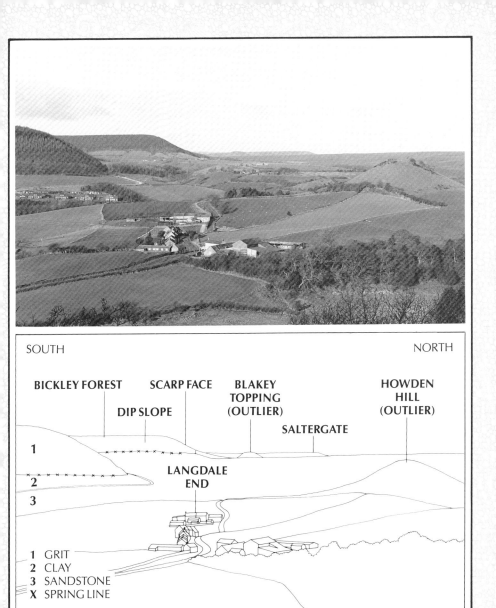

The Tabular Hills

Looking west from Broxa Bank (944912)

This is a 'text book' example of an escarpment and extends from the outskirts of Scarborough to Bilsdale in the west. The relationship between rocks, relief and land use is very striking. Forest has been developed on the poor soils of the steep, upper slopes, farming on the lower, more fertile soils. To the north, forest and moorland clothe the acid soils of the high moors.

— 29 —

scarp edge result in scrubland or coniferous forests except where, as near Saltergate, the land has been improved for farming.

The Hackness valley near Scarborough displays an intricate drainage pattern with many streams converging near Hackness village to flow south through Forge Valley and into the Vale of Pickering. The valley system has been likened to a splayed hand, and fingers representing the numerous valleys, the wrist and forearm the main channel draining through Forge Valley. With the exception of Forge Valley, there is no doubt that the Hackness Valley system had developed onto the dip slope of the Tabular Hills long before the onset of the Great Ice Age about two million years ago. Having cut down through the overlying limestones and grits, the streams would find their valleys begin to broaden when they reached the level of the Oxford Clay. At this point springs could develop along the junction of the clay and the overlying grits. It is this process of stream erosion and spring sapping that has developed the Hackness Valley as we see it today. In glacial times, when stream outlets on the coast were blocked by ice, a glacial lake developed in the Hackness Valley; this lake eventually overflowed to cut the distinct "V" shaped meltwater channel of Forge Valley through which the waters of the lake escaped into the Vale of Pickering.

—— The Western Scarp ——

The Hambleton Hills which form the south western boundary of the park are, geologically speaking, directly linked with the Tabular Hills. Their general dip, however, is towards the east which results in an impressive west facing escarpment overlooking the Vale of York. Sutton Bank, where the A170 climbs up the escarpment from Thirsk, is perhaps the best known location on this range of hills. The view is enhanced by Lake Gormire, a natural lake lying in a hollow at the foot of the bank. The hollow in which the lake lies was formed in the late glacial period as meltwater flowed south between the scarp foot and the huge ice sheet in the Vale of York. The same meltwater deepened the valley that today isolates Hood Hill from the scarp near the gliding station.

Lake Gormire

From Sutton Bank (514830)

The Hambleton Hills, a western extension of the Tabular Hills, terminate in a bold escarpment overlooking the Vale of York.

During the later part of the Great Ice Age, which ended only about 10,000 years ago, vast ice sheets, hundreds of feet in thickness, gradually spread from the north to cover much of the Vale of York.

As escaping water flowed southward it cut channels between the edge of the ice and the adjacent hills. Lake Gormire, the only natural lake in the park, has developed in part of one of these channels.

The White Horse of Kilburn

Aerial photograph looking north from 513805. (Crown Copyright)

The White Horse of Kilburn is a dramatic feature of the north west corner of the Hambleton Hills. Unlike similar figures in the south of England which are cut into chalk hillsides, the Kilburn horse exposes the buff-grey gritstones of the Middle Oolites. For this reason, after it was cut in 1857, it had to be coated in whitewash in order to brighten its appearance!

Recent maintenance involves spreading chalk chippings over the surface in defiance of the local geology!

A short distance from Sutton Bank is the famous White Horse of Kilburn. Unlike its counterparts in the south of England which are cut into turf on chalk hillsides the Kilburn White Horse was cut on a hillside consisting of grit and limestone. As a result, when the figure was cut in 1857, the outline had to be limewashed in order that it could be clearly seen. In more recent times chalk chippings from the Yorkshire Wolds have been used to achieve the same effect.

The northern limit of the Hambleton Hills is Black Hambleton overlooking Osmotherley. At 400 metres (1309 feet) Black Hambleton is the highest point on the Hambleton plateau.

From Osmotherley to Roseberry Topping, then eastwards towards Staithes, the scarp face of the Cleveland Hills is formed from the Upper Lias rocks capped with massive sandstones of the Ravenscar Group. Extensive quarrying has taken place along these hillsides particularly for the mineral alum. At Carlton Bank the old alum quarries and tips of burnt, pink shale can still be clearly seen.

One of the best known landmarks in the national park must surely be Roseberry Topping. Isolated from the Cleveland escarpment by natural processes of erosion, the Topping was modified by man in the 19th century when mining for ironstone on the lower slopes led to a landslip which gave the hill its dramatic south west face.

—— The Northern Moorlands ——

The northern moorlands are regarded as that largely heather covered tract of upland lying north of the Tabular Hills and bounded on west and east by the western escarpment and the coast respectively. The highest point reached by these hills, indeed anywhere within the moors, is the 454 metres (1490 feet) on Urra Moor in the west. Standing on this high point the land appears to slope very gently eastwards; in fact one is looking along a ridge which forms the principal watershed of the North York Moors from Urra Moor to the sea at Ravenscar. Travelling eastwards along this ridge the land slopes down to the north and south respectively. To the north the hills slope quite steeply into the Esk Valley while to the south the dip is more gentle towards the Tabular Hills and the Vale of Pickering.

Roseberry Topping (577124)

The moorlands of north-east Yorkshire are characterised by an almost level skyline. Of the few isolated hills, Roseberry Topping with its craggy south-west face is probably the best known. The capping of massive sandstone has slipped over the past 100 years as a result of mining for ironstone in the underlying Lias shale.

Falling Foss – Littlebeck (889035)

While the North York Moors are not renowned for waterfalls, those which do exist are particularly attractive. Any waterfall requires a hard lip over which to drop, in this locality formed from the Dogger – a resistant sandstone with high iron content. Beneath the Dogger the soft Alum Shale is easily eroded resulting in the waterfall with plunge pool at the base.

Unlike some other falls in the area, Falling Foss will not form an overhanging lip as the joints in the Dogger cause blocks to fall away soon after the overhang begins to develop. In other parts of the park waterfalls often develop where sandstone edges occur along valley sides.

Lying to the north and roughly parallel with the moorland watershed is the valley of the River Esk which drains its waters into the North Sea at Whitby. The Esk Valley separates the central moorlands from the Guisborough and Danby moors to the north.

The rocks which form these high moorlands belong to the Ravenscar Group and consist of massive sandstones with softer shales and occasional marine beds belonging to the Scarborough Formation. The harder sandstones form conspicuous "edges" or cliffs to many of the valley sides and are often frequented by rock climbers. The streams have cut deep valleys through to the softer Lias shales and the better soils and shelter associated with the valleys has given rise to a distinct farming pattern.

The Esk Valley has been considerably altered as a result of glacial activity. Down stream from Lealholm the present river follows a tortuous course as it makes its way over extensive glacial deposits. This area of the Esk Valley was completely over-ridden by ice while upstream from Lealholm the broad, flat valley suggests that this area was at one time occupied by a glacial lake, a theory put forward at the turn of the century. This theory suggested that when this lake filled it overflowed and the water escaped by a tortuous route down the Esk Valley and Newtondale. Many of the channels cutting across the hillsides around Goathland were thought to be formed by this process. Recent research now suggests a more complicated story where the upper Esk Valley was occupied by ice and many of the hillside channels were formed beneath, rather than around the edge of the ice sheets.

Newtondale, however, is still regarded as having been formed over a very short period of time by huge quantities of meltwater draining from the Whitby area.

The Wainstones (559036)

The massive sandstone which forms the crags or 'edges' along the escarpment and valley sides in the northern part of the park, belongs to the lowest members of the Ravenscar Group.

Eroded for centuries by ice, rain and wind, often into unusual shapes, these outcrops now attract climbers in increasing numbers.

The Bridestones – Staindale (873915)

Between the gritstone and limestone which form the upper surface of the Tabular Hills is a band of rock known as Passage Beds. At the Bridestones, this coarse, limey sandstone forms a number of outcrops some of which appear top-heavy as the softer, lower layers erode more rapidly than those above.

—— Glossary ——

ALUM   A complex "potash" or "sulphate" mineral found in the Upper Lias, extensively worked from the early 17th century until the middle of the 19th.

AMMONITE   An extinct, tentacled marine animal which lived in a chambered, flat coiled shell. Common throughout the Jurassic period.

BOULDER CLAY   The debris, usually brown clay carried by ice and deposited when the ice melted. Forms a superficial deposit often of considerable thickness particularly along coastal areas.

DYKE   A more or less vertical band of igneous rock originally intruded when in a molten state.

EROSION   The lowering of the land surface by natural processes.

ERRATICS   Pebbles or boulders transported from their original situations by ice movement.

ESCARPMENT   An inland cliff or steep slope formed by the erosion of gently dipping hard rocks or less commonly as a result of geological faulting.

FAULT   A natural fracture of the earth's crust along which the rocks have been displaced.

FOSSIL   The remains or traces of once living animals or plants found naturally embedded in the rocks.

IGNEOUS   Rocks formed from what was originally a molten mass.

JET — Fossilised wood preserved under particular conditions. The best quality jet is found in the Upper Lias rocks of the Whitby area.

JOINTS — Natural cracks in the strata along which no movement has taken place.

JURASSIC — A principle division of geological time to which the majority of local rocks belong.

LAVA — Molten rock which issues from a vent in the earth's crust.

MELTWATER CHANNEL — A valley carved by water flowing from a glacier or glacial lake.

METAMORPHIC — Rocks which have been considerably altered by intense pressure, heat or a combination of the two.

OOLITE — Sedimentary rocks, usually limestones, consisting of tiny rounded grains or ooliths, each oolith formed of concentric layers of calcium carbonate around a nucleus. Also used as a group name for certain strata in the Jurassic period.

RHOMB PORPHYRY — An igneous rock showing large diamond shaped crystals set in a fine-grained matrix.

SCHIST — A foliated metamorphic rock which can be split into thin plates or flakes.

SEDIMENTARY — Rocks compressed or/and cemented from sediment, e.g. sand, silt, clay, etc. Also includes organic limestones, coal, etc.

SPILLWAY — See meltwater channel.

SPRING SAPPING — The process whereby a spring erodes the head of its valley.

STRATA — Beds or layers of sedimentary rock.

Bibliography

British Museum (Natural History) 1975. *British Mesozoic Fossils*

Ellis, C. *Pebbles on the Beach.* Faber & Faber

Eyre, S.R. & Palmer, J., 1973. *The Face of North East Yorkshire.* Dalesman

Rawson, P.F. & Wright, J.K., 1992. *The Yorkshire Coast.* Geologists' Association Guide No.34.

Kendall, P.F. & Wroot, H.E. 1924. *The Geology of Yorkshire*

Kent, Gaunt & Wood, 1980. *Eastern England (BRG).* HMSO

North York Moors. *Ravenscar Geological Trail.* National Park

Rayner, D.H. & Hemingway, J.E., 1974. *The Geology and Mineral Resources of Yorkshire.* Yorkshire Geological Society

Swinnerton, H.H. Fossils. *New Naturalist.* Collins

Young, S., 1978. *Geology of the Yorkshire Coast.* Dalesman

Rocks of the North York Moors — A Poster Map

This 23″ x 16″ full colour poster map shows the distribution of principal rock types within the North York Moors National Park together with selected sections to indicate the underlying structure of the area.

The Jurassic System in North East Yorkshire.

This 23″ x 16″ chart presents an easy reference to the many geological names in current usage within the local Jurassic System.

Of interest to teachers, students and the layman, these attractive posters are available from the National Park Information Service.

Acknowledgement

The assistance of Dr. J.K. Wright in the preparation of this booklet is gratefully acknowledged.